CHILDREN OF MANY LANDS

Their Traditions, Customs and Way of Life

By Dana Bruce and Elizabeth F. McCrady

Fully Illustrated

THE PLATT & MUNK CO., INC.

Publishers • NEW YORK

CONTENTS

Wilhelmina of the Netherlands

LONG, long ago a little girl named Wilhelmina lived on a canal boat in the Netherlands. This low, flat country in Europe is also called Holland. It has many canals and ditches. Water from lakes and rivers and low-lying land runs into the ditches. That leaves the land between the ditches dry for gardens and homes.

Wilhelmina rode up and down the canal every day in the summer. In winter when the boat was frozen in, she skated on the ice. In the Netherlands everyone knows how to skate. Children skate to school. Sometimes women skate to market. Wilhelmina loved her skates.

In summer Wilhelmina's father took cheese from farms to the city in his boat. Sometimes he took tulips—red, yellow, and white. Again he took vegetables. Sometimes he took only passengers. Days on the canal boat were always busy and happy.

Wilhelmina had a friend named Katy. She lived in a red house beside the canal. She often rode to the city with Wilhelmina, but she had never lived on a boat.

Wilhelmina had never lived in a house on dry land. Her house was drawn along the canal by a horse, pulling on a heavy rope. Her brother Jan rode the horse along a path beside the canal. Her father sat at the front of the boat and steered it under bridges.

One day Katy stood at the door of the red house and called to Wilhelmina. "Mother would like to have you spend the night with me," she said. Wilhelmina's mother said she might go. So Jan stopped the horse and Wilhelmina stepped ashore. She climbed the steps to the top of the bank beside the canal. There Katy was waiting for her.

Then klomp, klomp, klomp, went the wooden shoes of the two little girls along the road to the house. Remember, this happened long, long ago. They did not wear leather shoes then in the Netherlands as they do today. Being well-mannered girls, Wilhelmina and Katy left their *klompen* outside the door. Wooden shoes made far too much noise and brought

mud into the house. Then the girls walked in their stocking feet over the scrubbed, white floor.

"Mmmmmm, I smell something good," said Katy.

"So do I," said Wilhelmina. They found Katy's mother making cookies in the clean, white kitchen.

"You may have these for a picnic," she said, "as soon as you have delivered the milk."

Today dogs are no longer used to help with the work in the Netherlands. But when Wilhelmina and Katy were little girls, they were. So now Katy fastened a big dog named Hans to a bright yellow cart. In the cart were brass cans full of fresh milk.

"Rattle, rattle, rattle," went the cart along the road.

"Klomp, klomp, klomp," went four little wooden shoes.

"Bow, wow, wow," barked Hans, as he pulled the cart.

When the cans were empty, Katy and Wilhelmina went home. Katy's mother gave them cookies and cheese and milk for a picnic. They took their lunch and their dolls and went into the fields. In the Netherlands, fields have ditches around

them instead of fences. Soon the black and white cows saw two little girls sitting beside a ditch splashing their bare feet in the water. They were giving their dolls rides in their wooden shoes.

"Let's look for pictures in the water," said Wilhelmina. "Mother calls them reflections."

"I see two little girls with white caps on their heads," said Katy.

"I see a big bird flapping its wings," said Wilhelmina.

"Oh, it's a stork!" exclaimed Katy. "I hope it will fly to our house and build a nest in the wagon-wheel Father put on the roof. That would bring us good luck."

After supper Katy's father told them stories about their country. He told how the North Sea used to spread over the land, spoil the crops, and drown many people. He told how great walls called dikes were built to keep the water from spreading over the land. He told about a city called Zaandam known everywhere for its many windmills. He told them Bible stories about the pictures on the tiles of the fireplace.

When it was bedtime he opened a sliding door in the wall. Behind it was a high bed that looked like a shelf. Our two little, blue-eyed Dutch girls slept there all night.

The next morning Katy's mother gave them some tarts. "Would you like to take these to the burgomaster's?" she asked. "They have a new baby there."

What fun! The girls were eager to see the new baby, so they started out. Wilhelmina carried the tarts. Katy led the way. The burgomaster's wife thanked them and showed them the baby.

From there, Katy and Wilhelmina went to the tulip fields. The fields were as gay as a rainbow. There were red and white and purple and pink and yellow tulips. The Netherlands is the tulip garden of the world. Katy and Wilhelmina enjoyed seeing the men cut the flowers.

When Wilhelmina's houseboat came, the tulips were loaded
on it, to be taken to the market in the city. As they rode
down the canal Katy and Wilhelmina saw many other boats
loaded with tulips. It was the beginning of the tulip festival.

There would be tulips everywhere. Today there were tulips even in the cheese market! The girls laughed with excitement.

The porters carried the cheeses on big trays into the Weigh House. There they were weighed on scales. Katy and Wilhelmina watched the other boats nearby and threw bread to the ducks in the canal. Soon it was time to leave.

That night Katy slept alone in her bed in the red house beside the canal. Wilhelmina slept in her bed in the houseboat on the canal. She looked out of the window, with its white curtains and flower boxes for tulips, and watched the lights in the houses, and in the water, too. Wilhelmina went sound asleep with this picture of a fairyland in her mind.

MATSU AND TARO OF JAPAN

Matsu and Taro of Japan

MATSU was a little Japanese girl, who lived on one of the islands of Japan in the northern Pacific Ocean.

Today was the happiest day of the year for Matsu—the Feast of the Dolls. This comes every year on the third day of the third month. Matsu awakened very early in the morning. She rolled up her bed and put it into a closet. Her bed is easily rolled up. It is just a soft quilt, which she spreads on the floor every night. She rests her neck on a pillow of wood which looks like a large letter "X."

"Taro, Taro," she cried to her little brother. "Get up. Today is the Feast of the Dolls." Taro's sleepy eyes blinked. This

was a holiday for girls, not for boys. His holiday would come on the fifth day of the fifth month.

Matsu and Taro put on their prettiest kimonos. Matsu was proud of her new sash. It was made of pink silk and was

very wide. The Japanese call a sash an *obi*.

"Now, children," said their father after breakfast, "come with me to the *kura*." The *kura* is a storehouse built of cement so that valuable things may be kept in it. Many Japanese families have such a *kura* in their gardens.

A Japanese house is not as sturdy as the *kura*. The walls of the house are of wood. Instead of windows, very often the daylight comes through panes of paper that permit only some of the light to come through. One at a time, the family's pretty vases and pictures are brought from the *kura* to be enjoyed in the house. Today Matsu put away one picture and took out another.

Matsu's father took two boxes down from the shelves in the *kura*. Matsu wanted to carry the small box. "Oh, no, honorable sister, you must let me carry that," said Taro politely. "I am a boy and I am strong." Matsu gave him the box without a word. Matsu's father carried the big box. In it, Matsu knew, were her special dolls.

Matsu carried her favorite picture rolled up in a scroll. It was of the highest mountain in Japan. The beautiful, snow-capped mountain is widely known as Fujiyama, but the Japanese themselves call it Fuji-san, for *san* means mountain.

"The shelves are ready for the *O-Hina* dolls," said Matsu's mother, when they reached the house. *O-Hina* means *"cherished* or *beloved* little object."

One by one Matsu took the dolls out of the big box. She had not seen them for a year. They were dolls with which her mother and her grandmother had played. In the center of the scarlet cloth on the shelves she put her Emperor and Empress dolls. Around them she put the other dolls. All were dressed in pretty silk kimonos.

In the small box Matsu found furniture and dishes for the dolls. She put tiny cakes in tiny dishes on tiny tables. Then she said, "I am ready to go."

Now Taro was really excited. For the first time in his life he was going to ride in a taxicab. Always before when Mother had taken him to the city to shop, they had gone in the big bus. But now a taxicab! He could just see them, honorable Father, Mother, Matsu and himself, in the cab, flying around corners, the horn blowing, brakes squeaking.

Of course they might have taken an old-fashioned rickshaw. However, nobody but visitors from other countries used uncomfortable rickshaws any more. Rickshaws were pretty to look at. Stagecoaches in America are interesting, too. But both rickshaws and stagecoaches are only bits of history left over from long ago.

Matsu loved the taxi ride almost as much as Taro. But she was eager to get to the doll shops. Honorable Mother wanted to shop for nylons first in the big shops in the Ginza shopping center. But she saw Matsu's eagerness to look at dolls so they went to the doll shops at once.

"Matsu," said her father, "You may have the doll you like

the best." There were so many beautiful dolls, how could she ever decide on one?

Finally she said, "I like this doll the very best." It was a little girl doll with a baby on her back.

"Thank you, most honorable father, for the doll," said Matsu politely. Japanese children are always polite.

As she looked at her new doll, Matsu turned to her young brother and said, "I carried you like that when you were a baby, Taro. You never fell out of the sash of my kimono, even when I played games."

"The doll's flowered kimono is just like yours," said Taro. "It has a red kimono underneath, too."

The Japanese family visited shop after shop and house after house to see beautiful dolls. At each house they left their wooden shoes or clogs outside the door. They bowed low and said *"Ohayo,"* which means "Good morning." When they left they bowed again and said, *"Sayonara,"* which means "Goodbye."

Now they went to one of the big department stores in the Ginza. The children could not even guess at what fun was in store for them. The store had a big theater where free performances of Japanese songs and dances were given all day. There was even a zoo with a huge Indian elephant! After Mother had finished her shopping, they went to see the puppet show.

Then it was time for lunch. Because it was such a special day, honorable Father took them all to a fine restaurant where they had a delicious lunch of *sukiyaki,* which is made of meat

and vegetables, and almond cakes and tea. Then it was time to go home, past the beautiful gardens of the Royal Palace.

What a wonderful day it had been, Matsu thought as she hugged her new doll all the way home.

When they reached home they left their clogs outside the door. Their feet, in fresh white *tabi*, pattered over the clean mats on the floor. *Tabi* are socks that look like mittens, with a special place for the big toe of each foot.

With their feet tucked under them on the floor, they ate their dinner of rice and fish from a very low table. Instead of using knives and forks the way we do, they ate with chopsticks. They drank tea from cups without handles.

After dinner the table was taken away. When bedtime came

a sliding door was pulled across a big room. This made two
small rooms. The wooden shutters were closed over the paper
walls.

As Matsu lay on her quilt, she whispered, "Taro, hasn't it been a wonderful day?"

"Yes," answered Taro. "Now I can hardly wait until the Feast of the Flags. I hope the boys on my side will capture all the flags from the other side. I'll see my soldier dolls again, too."

"Oh, I don't like battles," said Matsu. "Not even pretend battles. Do you know what I like best of all on your holiday? I like the big paper fish that are tied to the pole before our house."

"I wish we had a brother," said Taro. "Then we would have two paper fish, one for him and one for me."

When sleep came at last, Taro dreamed about the Feast of the Flags. And Matsu, like girls everywhere, dreamed about her dolls and the excitement she had shared with all her family on this special day, the Feast of the Dolls.

MANUEL
OF MEXICO

Manuel of Mexico

MANUEL is a little Mexican boy who helps his father on his farm north of Mexico City. His burro, Pedro, carries him into the fields to watch the sheep and goats. Manuel wears a big straw hat called a *sombrero*. It protects him from the hot sun. There are handsome *sombreros,* too, made of felt. But they are not for a boy working in the country.

Manuel's *sarape,* a gaily striped blanket for his head to go through, takes the place of an overcoat. In the city Manuel would not wear his *sarape.* But it is easy to wear when he rides. Under it he wears coarse cotton clothes.

Manuel is one of thirty-three million proud Mexicans who live in beautiful Mexico. For three hundred years Spain ruled Mexico. Then Mexico decided to rule itself. Many Mexicans

are either of pure Indian or pure Spanish blood. Others are descended from a long-ago Indian mother and Spanish father.

If you look at the map of Mexico you will find it looks like a big horn of plenty. Indeed it is a horn of plenty! When the Spaniards took it away from the Indians over four hun-

dred years ago, they did not know how rich it was. Mexico is only about one fourth as large as the United States, but it has many sorts of riches.

Today you may see there the beautiful pictures of many artists. And where are there such lovely pieces of wood carving or silver work? We have seen one of the farms where sheep and goats are raised. But that is only one part of the country. In the mountains there are silver mines. In yet other parts there are rubber, tobacco, and cotton plantations. And almost everywhere there are men and women busy making fine baskets and weaving colorful fabrics. Some day when Manuel grows up and leaves his father's farm, he may be a great artist. Like many American boys, he may go to the city. But he will never forget his happy days riding over the fields on little Pedro.

Manuel's mother, like all farmers' wives, is busy from

morning until night. Their little house is made of adobe, a sun-baked clay. It is cool in the summer and warm in the winter. When Mother is not busy cleaning, she is cooking for her family.

If she should invite you to dinner, do not expect ordinary bread and butter. Instead, you would get some freshly baked *tortillas* or corn cakes. Manuel's mother took a great deal of trouble to make them. Kneeling on the floor, she ground the corn between two stones for hours. Then she patted the paste into cakes and baked them.

Mother's dress is of cotton. Out of doors she never wears a hat. Instead, her head is covered with a shawl called a *rebozo*. It is soft and sometimes she carries Manuel's baby sister in it. In the city one may see beautiful and costly *rebozos* worn by ladies there, too.

Let us say goodbye to Manuel and his mother and leave

the dry plains with their prickly cactuses for another part of
Mexico. Before we come to Mexico City, the capital of the
country, there are miles and miles of great stiff plants growing far higher than your head. You may have seen a single
plant like these in the center of a wide lawn and called it a

century plant. Mexicans call it the maguey and they think a great deal of it. No wonder, for the maguey gives them all sorts of useful things for their homes.

Now, let us join young Alphonso as he rides toward his house. The house is in a green valley. Here in the courtyard

Alphonso's little sister, Tessa, is sitting in the shade, sewing her doll's dress. Tessa has her duties, too. She feeds the chickens and helps Mother grind the corn for *tortillas*. Now she hopes Alphonso will come soon. Maybe he will take her when he and Father collect the maguey sap!

In Mexico they make ropes from the fibres of the maguey leaves and braid them into mats for tables and chairs. They make a fire of the part of the plant which cannot be used for anything else, and over it they cook the roots which they use for food.

But Mexicans grow the maguey plant mainly for its juice. They call it "honey water," and from it make a drink called *pulque*.

Who shall say where this nectar got its name? It is now a part of Mexico. The people of Mexico take the juice from the plant in a strange way. Just before the plant is ripe, they

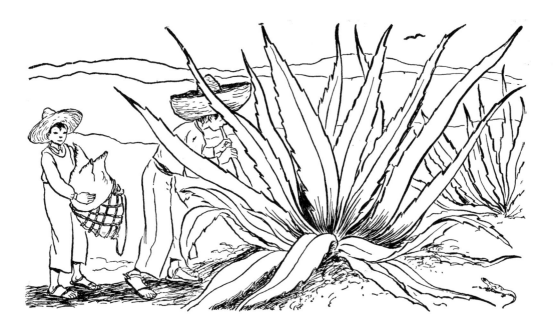

cut out the center of the stem. A hollow is left as big around as a washbowl. The sweet sap runs into this hollow. Two or three times a day little Alphonso comes with his father to get it. Alphonso's father puts one end of a long, thin gourd in the bowl of sap, then with his lips at the other end, he draws up the sap into the gourd. Next he pours the sap into a pigskin and hangs it over his shoulders; or he carries it away in jars on a donkey's back.

As you leave the maguey plantation behind, you come into Mexico City. This beautiful city, like every other Mexican town, has a park called a plaza in its center. There is a bandstand where the people come evenings and Sunday mornings to listen to the music they love. A very large and beautiful cathedral faces the plaza. There are many fine churches in Mexico.

The houses with their high stone walls and heavy iron bars

look very gloomy. These are the old houses built in the old Spanish manner. Long ago such gloom stood for strength and grandeur, nothing more. Inside, how bright everything is! The house is built around a courtyard or *patio*. Here there are trees and a fountain. Here the children of the family play.

Carmen and Miguel, the city children who live here, invite you to share their Christmas with them. Christmas Day is not the time for fun in Mexico, however. It is a Holy Day. Many families have their own beautiful *crêche* or *nancimiento*. In Mexico, the fun and gifts come later, on January sixth or Twelfth-Night.

The *piñata* is part of the frolic. It is a big jar covered with bright paper to look like a big doll or bird. The children are blindfolded and take turns trying to smash the *piñata*. What a scramble when the candy, nuts, and small gifts tumble out!

So we see that children everywhere work and play. None of us is very different from the other. Manuel rides his burro. Maybe you ride a bike. Alphonso helps with the maguey. Perhaps you run errands for Mother. Carmen and Miguel play in the *patio*. You play in the back yard.

Mexico is a great country. Mexico is our good neighbor. Let us learn to work and play together.

CHULA OF THAILAND

Chula of Thailand

CHULA is a little boy who lives in Thailand, an ancient country in Asia. Sometimes it is called the Land of the White Elephant. Chula likes his nation's flag better than any other in the whole world. It has two stripes of red, two stripes of white, and a broad stripe of blue across the center.

There are many elephants in Thailand. Some are dark gray and some are light gray. The dark gray elephants work in the forests. The lighter-colored elephants are known as sacred white elephants. They are given to the king and are royally treated in a palace of their own.

In Thailand there are many little boys like Chula, and of course many little girls, too. Some of the children drive big water buffalo when the rice fields are plowed. The boys wade in water, as they put the rice plants into the muddy ground. When the rice is ripe it is taken to the city in boats. Rice is the most important crop grown in Thailand, for it supplies

much of the food of the more than twenty million people of that country.

Other boys and girls live in houseboats on the river. When they want to buy something, they go in their teakwood canoes to a store floating on water. As they go up and down

the river they pass many beautiful temples. If a canoe tips over, the children do not mind. They learn to swim almost as soon as they walk, and so they are happy in the water.

Some boys and girls live near great forests of teak trees. That is where Chula lives. Every year there are heavy rains and floods. Chula's house is on stilts made of teakwood. Teakwood has so much oil in it that it does not rot in water. The stilts keep the house high and dry. The roof is made of palm leaves. In dry weather Chula's father keeps his animals under the house in the space created by the stilts.

"Wake up," said Chula's father one bright morning. "We are going into the forest to cut timber."

Chula's father spoke softly in words that sound much like Chinese. The language of Thailand is especially interesting. Each word has as many as five different meanings when it is spoken in different tones of voice.

Chula arose from his mat on the floor. The air was very warm. Around his waist he tied his *panung,* which is a wide strip of colored cloth. Many Thai boys and men still wear the *panung* instead of trousers, but the *panung* is not seen as much now as in the olden days.

In a few minutes Chula and his father and two other men were on their way to the forest. When they came to a tall, straight tree on a low hill, Chula's father stopped to look at it. Its leaves were dead.

"What is that ring around the trunk of the tree?" asked Chula.

"That is the girdle," said his father. "I cut the bark that way to make the tree die slowly. After the tree is dead it is light enough to float on water."

Then one man started to chop on one side of the tree, while the second woodsman chopped on the other side. The notches they made got bigger and bigger. At length the top of the tree moved a little. The men ran quickly to safety, as the tall tree fell to the soft ground.

"Now, Chula," said his father, "help us chop the tree into logs." All day Chula worked near his father.

The next morning Chula was glad when his father said, "Today we will take the elephants with us to the forest."

In a few minutes Chula sat on the back of his favorite

elephant, Bumpo, so called because he bumped logs into
place with his ivory tusks and sometimes even with his head.

"I like you better than any other elephant in the whole
world," whispered Chula, as Bumpo's big feet went crashing
over the underbrush of the forest.

"Thailand has more teak forests than any other country
in the world," said Chula's father, as he rode on his elephant. Chula said nothing. He was thinking how lucky he
was to live near a teak forest in Thailand.

"You start on the logs at that end," said Chula's father,
when they came to the freshly cut logs on the ground. "And
if Bumpo does not work, prod him with your stick."

But Bumpo knew what to do. He had been working in
the teak forest for many years. With a chain, Chula fastened
a log to Bumpo's harness. The elephant dragged the log
slowly for three miles to the river bank. Then back he went

for another log. He used his trunk and his tusks to put the logs in a neat pile.

Back and forth, back and forth, went the elephants, dragging logs to the banks of the river. Soon the logs would be floated down the river to the sawmill.

"I like to do this," said Chula to his father.

"Yes," said his father, "today the elephants are doing the hard work. But you must learn to like hard work, too."

Finally Chula's father said, "Elephants are not as strong as they look. They should not work more than four hours a day." So Chula and Bumpo stopped working. Bumpo ate banana leaves and bamboo sprouts. Chula ate mangosteens, a fruit which grows in Thailand.

Chula said, "Bumpo, you are hot and tired. How would you like a bath in the river?"

Bumpo nodded his head and looked pleased. He went

splashing into the water. First his feet were wet, then his
ankles, then his knees. He filled his trunk with water and
squirted it all over Chula. Chula liked the nice, cool shower.
Then Bumpo lay down in the river. Chula started to scrub
him with a brush of twigs. He scrubbed and scrubbed, until

he had one side of Bumpo all clean, except his great big ear.

Just as he was trying to get to the ear, Bumpo sneezed, "Kerchoo!" He sneezed so hard that he shook all over, and Chula slipped off his side, right into the water. As fast as he could, Bumpo stood up and held out his trunk toward Chula. Then Bumpo lifted Chula out of the water, and with Chula on his back, Bumpo walked slowly out of the river, making a loud "splash, splash, splash, splash."

On the way home, Chula said, "Bumpo, you are a kind friend. I would rather have you than the finest white elephant of the king's herd. You deserve a palace and robes of silk and jewels on your back."

Bumpo shook his head. He had grown fond of the boy who had shown such care for him, and Bumpo was thinking that he would rather work in the forest with Chula than live in the finest palace.

KARI
OF NORWAY

Kari of Norway

"FATHER, may I go fishing with you today?" asked Kari, a little girl who lived in Norway.

"Yes," said her father, "you may come along, but you must put on your warmest clothes."

In a few minutes Kari was ready. You could see only two blue eyes and a little nose in a bundle of wool. Kari and her father slipped their feet into the loops on their long, narrow skis. They carried long sticks to keep their balance. Then they went skimming over the top of the snow. Norway is a country so far north that there is deep snow all winter. Kari learned to ski almost as soon as she learned to walk.

Soon they came to a fjord. A fjord is a long, narrow inlet from the sea. In winter, ice forms at the foot of the fjord where fresh water from the mountains blends with warm

water from the Gulf Stream.

There were ice boats and many skaters there now. Fish were swimming under the ice. Now Kari's father prepared for the exciting sport. First he chopped a round hole in the

ice. Then he put beside the hole a stick that could easily be bent. That was to be his fishpole. To this he tied his fishing line. There were many hooks on the line. Each hook was a bright color. Down into the water went the hooks without any bait.

"Now we shall wait for a bite," said Kari's father. "This tent I have put on the ice will keep the cold wind from us."

Suddenly he said, "Look, Kari, the pole is wiggling up and down." Kari watched him pull the line up out of the water. On it were many wiggly, waggly fish.

"One, two, three, four, five, six, seven, eight, nine, ten, eleven, twelve!" Kari counted. "I wish I could catch twelve fish at one time."

"You can," answered her father, "but first we must take these fish off the hooks." Off came the slippery fish and zip, into a basket.

All afternoon Kari and her father took turns fishing, until they had all the fish they could carry. It was dark when they started home. The winter days in Norway are very short. "See the northern lights!" said her father.

Kari smiled and said, "I am glad I live way up north. I look for the northern lights every winter night. I pretend that the sky fairies dance along those beautiful streaks of pink and yellow and white in the sky."

"To me," said her father, "they look like bright ribbons in the sky."

Northern lights are caused by electricity in the air. There are many different gases in the air near the North Pole. When the electricity strikes these gases, it causes many beautiful colors to appear in the sky.

Kari and her father and mother ate some of their fish for dinner. With it they ate such strange-looking bread. It was large and round and quite flat. It is called *fladbrod*.

One day Kari's mother said, "Spring is coming. The days are

getting longer. The snow has melted off the mountains. Tomorrow we will take the animals to the fresh, green grass
up there."

Kari was glad it was time to go to the dairy pasture in

the mountains. All winter long she had played with the toys her father had carved for her out of wood. Now she could be in the lovely, green mountains and play on the moss, beside the sparkling streams.

Early the next morning, a long parade of farm animals started up the mountain. There were horses and cows, and calves and sheep and goats and pigs. In front of the parade the head milkmaid rode on a horse. She sat on a high saddle. She wore a white kerchief on her head.

Kari walked behind the animals, carrying her lunch in a knapsack on her back. With a heavy stick she kept the animals in line. Up, up, they went over the stony mountain roads. Finally they came to the *saeter,* the dairy farm in the mountains. How happy Kari was to see the *saeter* log cabin with flowers growing on its grass roof! In the distance she could

see snow-capped mountains.

All summer her work seemed like play to her. Every morning and evening she helped milk the cows and goats. Then the milk was put into a small barrel or churn. Kari turned the handle round and round until the milk turned to butter.

Sometimes goat cheese was made in large iron pots. When the water in the goat's milk had boiled away, the milk turned brown. Goat cheese looks like big pieces of brown soap. Cow's milk was cooked in iron kettles until it turned into cheese. There was white, yellow, and pink cheese. Everyone on the *saeter* was kept busy from morning till night, storing food for the long winter.

Kari liked to help in the hay fields. She picked up the hay and put it on the wooden racks. There the sun and air dried it. One day it would be food for the animals.

In the evening Kari played her little birchbark pipe. Then it was fun to dance the folk dances of Norway.

Some days in June were so long that there was no night at all. At midnight the sun shone brightly. At times children from another *saeter* came to visit. They had many good times picking wild flowers and berries.

There came a day when summer was over. Tubs filled with cheese and butter were packed on the horses. The parade started down to the red farmhouse in the lowlands. There the butter and cheese would be stored in the wooden storehouse or *stabbur*, for the long, cold winter. The *stabbur* was built on high thick poles to keep wild animals from stealing the food. Kari said *"Farvel"* (farewell) to the *saeter* she loved so dearly.

CHING LING
AND TING LING

Ching Ling and Ting Ling

CHING LING is a little boy who lives in China. Ching Ling has a chubby little sister. Her name is Ting Ling.

Every day Ching tells Ting about something he did in school that day. One day after school Ching cried, "Ting, look, look!" Ting ran to see what he had to show her. Ching unrolled a piece of paper. On it were two Chinese words. They did not look like our words. They looked like designs. "I learned to write these today," said Ching. "I made them with brush and ink."

"Oh, please show me how you made them," asked Ting.

Ching was happy to do that. He took from his silk purse a thick, flat stick of dried ink. It looked like licorice. He rubbed the dried ink in a few drops of water, on a flat stone. Then he painted this sign +, like two sticks crossed. "That means ten," said Ching. Then he painted this sign ⊹. "That

means rice." Ching must learn thousands of such picture letters, because the Chinese do not have ABC's as we have.

"I'll be glad when I am old enough to go to school," sighed
Ting.

"Now, little sister," said Ching, "come with me. I am going to fly my new kite."

Soon Ting and Ching were walking up the hill with the kite. Finally Ching said, "Now, watch my bird of happiness." The kite did look like a bird. It had green eyes, red wings, and a striped purple and blue tail. "I call it my bird of happiness," said Ching, "because it sings when it flies through the air."

Ting's small, slanting eyes looked puzzled as she said, "I didn't know a kite could sing."

"This bird of happiness can," answered Ching. "Just listen when she is flying high." Ching unwound the kite string that was around a stick. Along came a rushing breeze. It lifted the bird of happiness. Together the breeze and the bird went dancing, prancing in the sunlight. "Listen, Ting," said Ching.

Ting cocked her head on one side and listened. Then

she smiled and said, "I hear the bird." Sure enough, a lovely, soft, whistling sound floated down from the sky. "What makes the paper bird sing?" asked Ting.

"I fastened a reed onto the kite," explained Ching. "It is a piece of coarse grass. When the wind blows on the reed, it makes that lovely sound."

"The bird is dancing to the music," said Ting, looking very pleased.

Ching laughed. He looked up at his kite. "Yes, it is hopping around like a dancing bird."

Just then Ching and Ting saw something strange, walking up the hill. It looked like a big goldfish, but of course, a goldfish can't walk up hills. It was a big paper kite. Behind it was a little boy. "Let's have a battle with our kites," said the little boy, whose name was Ho.

"Oh yes," agreed Ching, "let's try to cut each other's kite

strings in half."

"How can you do that?" asked Ting.

"Look here," said Ho. "I dyed my string black so that it can easily be seen while the kite is flying. Then I glued pow-

dered glass to it. That makes the string sharp enough to cut another string." Ting still looked puzzled but she waited and watched.

Soon Ho had his bright goldfish swimming through the

air. "I hear a tinkle, tinkle," said Ting. "What is it?"

"That is from the bells fastened on my kite," explained Ho.

Ho and Ching held tightly to their kite sticks. Each one wanted to win the battle. Each one wanted to prove his skill.

Now the fish and bird were side by side. Ho tried to work his string over Ching's string. Ching tried to cross Ho's string with his own sharp one.

The bird flew up and down, back and forth. The goldfish darted forward and backward, now sideways, now up and down. The bells tinkled merrily. The whistle made sweet sounds. Ting jumped up and down with excitement. Ching and Ho were breathless.

Suddenly the bird of happiness flew up, up in the air. It had been cut free. Ho's goldfish had won the game. Ching was sorry he had lost, but he was a good sport. He praised

Ho for his skill.

Ting and Ching looked a little sad, as they watched that beautiful bird-kite fly away. The wind was carrying it over the hills. It seemed to get smaller and smaller. Now the bird of happiness was out of sight.

Then Ho, Ting, and Ching started to walk slowly down the hill.

"I'll help you make a new kite," said Ho.

"That would be kind of you," said Ching. "I'll buy some rice paper, bamboo sticks, paste, and string tomorrow. See, I have saved some money." He reached in his pocket and pulled out a string. On the string were four Chinese pieces of money. They had square holes in the center. That is how they could be carried on a string.

Ching and Ting were hungry when they ate their rice din-

ner that night. The Chinese eat rice every day. Sometimes, when Chinese meet along the street, instead of saying, "How do you do?" they say, *"Chihfahn,"* which means "Have you eaten rice?" Ching and Ting lifted their bowls of rice and meat to their lower lips. Then they pushed the food into their mouths with chopsticks, which the Chinese use as we use forks and spoons.

After dinner it was story time. Their father read a story to them. He started from the back page of the book. He read up and down on the page, instead of back and forth. That is the way the Chinese read.

Soon Ting's head nodded. Ching was sleepy, too. They had had a busy day. Off they went to bed. You would never guess of what their beds are made. They are made of bricks! In winter a fire is made under the brick beds to keep the sleepers warm. Now Ching Ling and Ting Ling have been tucked safely under soft covers. Let's say, *"How foon."* That means "Good night" in Chinese.

MARIA AND CARLOS
OF SPAIN

Maria and Carlos of Spain

"MARIA, MARIA," cried Carlos, a boy who lives in Spain. "Come quickly, I have a surprise for you." Carlos was walking through the iron gates which led from the street to the courtyard of his home. He looked up at the balcony around the courtyard. From one of the rooms up there, his little sister came running.

She soon stood beside her big brother, by the fountain in the courtyard. The courtyard in Spain is called the *patio*. Around it the Spanish house is built. The *patio* is like a garden. There are orange and lemon trees in it. There are baskets of flowers hanging from the balconies around it. There are cages filled with singing birds.

"Can you guess what I have for you?" asked Carlos.

"A red rose for my hair," Maria guessed, her black eyes flashing.

"No," answered Carlos.

"Perhaps you met a *barquillero* on the street and paid him

to turn the wheel. When his wheel stopped, the hand pointed to the number two, so he gave you two little cakes, one for you and one for me. Am I right, Carlos?" asked Maria.

"Wrong again," said Carlos. "Here it is." He took his hands from behind his back. In them he held a box. It was dripping wet. No wonder!

When Maria opened the box she cried, "Oh, goldfish! Two beautiful goldfish for our pool!"

"Let's put them into the fountain," Carlos said. So he held the box upside down, over the little pool in the *patio*. Splash, splash, went the two little goldfish, into their new home.

"Soon you will have a roof of blue sky," said Maria to her new pets. "The awning over our *patio* will be taken away when the days grow cooler."

Spain is a country in southern Europe and it gets very hot there. The hot part of the day is called "hours of fire."

Then the children do not play in the streets but stay in the shade of the *patio*.

While Maria and Carlos were watching the goldfish, their father came to them. "I must drive to the vineyards today," he said. "Who would like to go with me?"

"I would," cried Maria, for she had never been to the vineyards.

"I would, too," said Carlos, "but I promised to be in a bull fight this afternoon." (He meant a pretend bull fight, of course.)

Soon Maria and her father were driving to the country. Maria's sharp eyes saw everything. Suddenly she said, "I see a walking straw stack."

"A walking straw stack?" said her father. "Who ever heard of a walking straw stack?" He looked ahead and there he saw a little mule so covered with straw, that it did look like a

straw stack. In Spain the mules carry all sorts of things.
Sometimes, they even carry children to school.

As they drove along, Maria and her father munched on
ripe olives. Like most Spaniards, they like to eat olives at all

times. There are so many olive orchards in Spain, that Spanish olives are sent all over the world.

When they came to the vineyards, Maria saw men, women, and children at work. They were picking bunches of pink

and purple grapes from the vines and filling large baskets.

"Where are they going?" asked Maria, looking at the women carrying tall baskets on their heads.

"They are going to the sorting shed, to sort the grapes," answered her father. "They will put the very best ones into one wagon and the other grapes into another."

"There are some wagons filled with grapes," said Maria.

"Yes," answered her father. "Those are going to the wine-press. There the grapes are crushed to make wine."

Maria watched, while her father talked business with a man there. When they started home, her father gave her a large bunch of raisins. "You may eat these on your way home," he said. "They are grapes which have been dried."

"I'll save them for Carlos," said Maria. "He brought me a present this morning. I'll give him a present tonight."

Suddenly her face looked as bright as the sun, and she cried, "Oh, I hear the piper, I hear the piper with his pigs. What a queer tune he is playing on his pipe!"

Down the road came a man, with many pigs trotting behind him. There were little ones and big ones, fat ones and thin ones. There were many pink noses and curly tails.

"They have been looking for acorns all day under the cork oaks in the mountain," said Maria's father. "Acorns make thin pigs fat and fat pigs fatter. The cork oak is a very useful tree."

"Why is it so useful?" asked Maria.

"Men cut the bark off the cork oaks every ten years," explained her father. "They soak it in water, then clean it and scrape it and heat it and press it out in flat sheets. After that

the cork is made into stoppers for bottles and many other things."

"Some of the pigs leave the others and run down different lanes," said Maria.

"Yes," answered her father, "each pig seems to know when he comes to his own home. He runs to it without being driven."

"There are the gypsies in their strange homes," said Maria, pointing to caves which the gypsies had made in the side of a rocky hill.

"Yes," her father replied, "and soon we shall be in our home. Each one thinks his home is best, doesn't he?"

That night after their dinner of *tortillas* or corn cakes, fruit, and hot chocolate, Maria's father played his guitar while Maria danced in the *patio*. Watching her dance, Carlos munched on the raisins which Maria had given him as a present. It was the end of a long and wonderful day!

KALA OF HAWAII,
OUR FIFTIETH STATE

Kala of Hawaii,

Our Fiftieth State

KALA lives on the island of Oahu, far out in the Pacific Ocean. Oahu is a part of Hawaii, which is not a foreign land at all (although many years ago it was, until it became a territory of the United States). Now, Hawaii – which actually is a group of beautiful islands – is the fiftieth state of the Union.

Kala's skin is brown from the warm sun. He is descended from the proud island people who lived in the Pacific islands centuries ago. Kala goes to a fine school. He speaks English, of course, but unlike many other American children of his own age he speaks another language, too – Hawaiian. The Hawaiian language is very musical. There are only 12 letters in the Hawaiian alphabet: a, e, h, i, k, l, m, n, o, p, u, and w.

One morning Kala's father said: "Kala, we need your help
in the pineapple fields today. Come along with me."

Kala had sometimes helped to gather ripe pineapples, but
he had never before helped to plant them. In the pineapple

fields he saw many long, wide strips of paper.

"How did you place the paper in such straight rows?" asked Kala.

"We laid the paper on the ground yesterday with a machine," answered his father. "The edges of the paper are held down by loose earth. The paper will keep the weeds from growing up around the plants. It will also keep the roots damp and warm."

"But how can pineapples grow up through the paper?" asked Kala.

"That is going to be your job, Kala," said his father. "Here is a tool for you. If you make holes in the paper, I will put the plants through the holes into the ground."

"Oh, that would be fun," said Kala, his black eyes sparkling. So up and down the rows of heavy paper, Kala punched holes with the tool. His father went behind him and planted small green pieces, cut from ripe pineapple plants.

"In about twenty months," said Kala's father, "there will be hundreds of ripe pineapples here, one on each plant."

"That is a long time for the plant to grow," said Kala.

"The plant is low," replied his father, "and it grows slowly. The pineapple grows on top of a short, thick stem in a nest of stiff, sharp leaves. The best pineapples in the world are grown here in the Hawaiian Islands. Most of them are canned before they are sent to other countries."

The sun was hot. Kala sang as he worked, for all Hawaiians like to sing. When he was thirsty he ran over to a palm tree to get a drink. Now, how could Kala get a drink from a tree? He ran up the trunk of the tree, holding on with his hands. Hawaiians can easily climb the trunks of the cocoanut trees because the trunks slope gradually. Kala came down with a brown cocoanut. He pulled off the husks and

made two holes in the cocoanut shell. Then he held it up to
his mouth. Down his hot throat trickled the juice of the
cocoanut. "Mmmmmm," said Kala, "that tastes better than
water."

After Kala and his father had worked a long time, Kala's father said, "Let's have a swim in the ocean."

Kala's face beamed with smiles, for he would rather swim than do anything else. Children in Hawaii learn to swim

when they are very young. Soon Kala and his father were splashing in the waves of the ocean. Each carried with him a smooth board, called a surfboard. When Kala got past the white splashing of the waves he stopped. He waited for a big wave, then quickly threw himself full length on the surfboard. The wave rolled nearer. Finally it lifted Kala's surfboard on its crest. Then swiftly it carried the surfboard and its rider to shore.

"I wish I could stand on my surfboard," said Kala as he watched his father ride his surfboard standing up.

"You can," his father answered, "if you try."

So the next time Kala tried to stand up on his swiftly moving surfboard. He was almost straight up when he lost his balance. He fell into the water and his surfboard reached the shore without a rider.

"Oh, I can't learn to do that," said Kala.

"Yes, you can," said his father. "You must not give up so easily. Try again."

So Kala tried again and again. Finally, he learned to stand on the board all the way to shore. That made him very happy and his father very proud.

When Kala got home he called to his little sister: "Liliha, Liliha, guess what I learned today. I learned to ride standing up on my surfboard, and I learned to plant pineapples. Now, close your eyes and hold out your hands, and I'll give you a surprise."

Little Liliha held out her hands. Into them Kala dropped a lovely pink shell. When Liliha opened her eyes and saw the shell she gave a cry of delight.

"Now, Kala," she said, "I have a surprise for you. Close your eyes."

Kala closed his eyes. He felt a lei or garland of flowers being put around his neck. When he opened his eyes he said, "Liliha, this the prettiest lei I ever have seen."

Liliha looked pleased. "I gathered the brightest flowers I

could find and made them into this lei for you," she said.

The two happy Hawaiian children went into their little house for dinner. They had fish, baked bananas, and poi. Poi is a pink porridge, made out of the taro plant.

After dinner Father said, "How would you two children like to go to Hawaii, the largest island of the Hawaiian group tomorrow?"

"Oh," cried Liliha, "I have always wanted to go to the island of Hawaii."

"So have I," said Kala. "I have always wanted to see the mountain there, that pours out melted rock and steam."

"Very well," said their father, "I will take you. You will see the largest volcano in the world. It is like a huge bowl in the earth. The bottom of it is like a lake of fire."

Kala and Liliha were excited and happy. That night they said "*Aloha Oe*" (Farewell) to one pleasant day and looked forward to the dawn of the next.